Zany Zoo Adventures in Writing

Jan May

New Millennium Girl Books

Zany Zoo Adventures in Writing–Homeschool Edition ©
2015 by Jan May
Copyright 2015, Jan May

Education and Language Arts

Printed in the United States of America
ISBN 978-0-9835281-8-0

Published by New Millennium Girl Books
690 Laurel Drive
Aurora, IL 60506

Clipart by

Educlips-www.loveeducasong.blogspot.com and

Contents

Introduction-Teacher's Notes

How to Get the Most from these Lessons

I have taught creative writing for over fifteen years and have found that given the right tools, any child can write and love it. I always stress creativity over grammar, and I praise every small effort made. I encourage parent-child brainstorming and fun activities for each lesson, thus creating a "writing adventure" instead of a dull writing lesson. I have discovered that keeping these things in mind, even the most reluctant writer will dive into the writing pool!

There are twelve easy lessons with a handout and activity for each lesson, where the individual student or family creates a zoo full of fanciful characters that can talk after the zoo keeper goes home each night. Each child picks a zoo animal character to become and writes from that point of view. Instruct students to personalize the animals by drawing clothing on them, adding sunglasses and accessories, mustaches or eyelashes. Each student will create a **character profile,** where they develop a personality and choose an occupation for their animal in the zoo community such as: mayor, cupcake baker, athlete, ballerina, military captain, etc.

Give the students a special folder to keep their story pages and illustrations in. Zoo stickers are a lot of fun to decorate the notebook with and can be found at a local teacher's' or dollar store.

Creative writing time can also be enhanced by geography, history, reading or art. This is a great time to study scientific classification with zoo animals, incorporate animal art projects, or write simple reports.

Encourage the students to find fun facts to share with the family or co-op and have a contest to see who can find the most interesting ones.

Brainstorming with the students for story ideas and plots creates a community spirit, and you will find the children begging for writing time. Kids have terrific ideas of what they are interested in.

Seasonal holiday themes always makes good story starters:

- Snow Day fun, sledding, snowmen
- Valentine's Day party
- St. Patrick's Day parade –illustrate a float
- Easter preparations, egg hunts
- School's out for summer, picnics, hiking, camping, vacations
- Fall fun, bonfires, football games, soccer
- Christmas stories of giving, animals' Christmas party

Stick with a theme for several weeks, then switch to another one. By the end of that time, the students will have several short stories they have written. Have the students illustrate their stories and read parts out loud along the way. Encourage them to include other students' characters in their stories in the family or class. This enhances story ideas and community. Each student can put it all together in a three-hole essay folder with a plastic cover.

Play "Story Beach Ball" at any point during the lessons so the children can share what they are writing. Write questions about the elements of a story in different colors on each section of the beach ball with a magic marker. Have the students bat the ball to each other. When you say "stop," the child who holds the ball will answer the question that his right thumb is on. The questions are:
- Who are the main characters in your story?
- What is the setting of your story?
- What is the story problem?
- Are you SHOWING and NOT TELLING?
- What is your story's solution?

End the unit with a Flashlight Theatre celebration. The children can bring flashlights, turn out the lights, and shine them on the reader (and bring snacks!). Each child can read their stories. It's a highlight of every semester in my classes. Invite friends, grandparents, or neighbors.

Lesson One Teacher's Notes
Create a Character

Have each student choose one zoo animal to become and write from that animal's point of view. They can page through the Animal Information Station sheets in the back of this book to learn about each animal and decide. Use catchy alliterations for names by using the same first letter sound such as Jimmy the Giant Giraffe, Larry the Lazy Lion, or Kelly the Crazy Kangaroo.

A good story helps the characters grow. They should have a few weaknesses to be realistic. If the characters start out selfish, give them opportunities to learn how to give. If they are fearful, give them a situation where they learn to face their fears and gain courage. Have the student fill out the Character Trail on page 10.

NOTE-Lessons one to five are for prewriting and priming the pump of creativity. They are necessary parts of the writing process. Most students will become very excited during these lessons. It is important for you, the teacher, to lead the students in brainstorming ideas for the characters and create a buzz about what is happening daily in your newly formed Zoo City. It becomes a community adventure that all the children will enjoy. Even the reluctant writer will dive in!

Activity-Zoo Animal Report
All professional writers do research. Have the students research their zoo animal and write a short science report. Have them include **zoo related words** that they find to use in their stories. Start a contest on who can find the most zoo related words. Use the **My Zoo Report** on the next page.

Notes_____

_____

_____

My Zoo Animal Report

Which animal did you choose?

_____

Where does it live?

_____

Describe where your animal lives.

_____

_____

What does it eat?

_____

_____

Describe your zoo animal: size, color, special features

_____

_____

_____

_____

How does it move? Crawl, hop, lumber, fly, etc.

_____

_____

_____

_____

To which scientific class does it belong?

_____

To which scientific family does it belong?

_____

Fun Facts

_____
_____
_____
_____

Other Interesting Facts

_____
_____
_____
_____
_____
_____
_____
_____
_____
_____
_____
_____

Follow the character trail. First write the name of your character in the circle. Then follow the arrows and write the answer to the questions in the boxes.

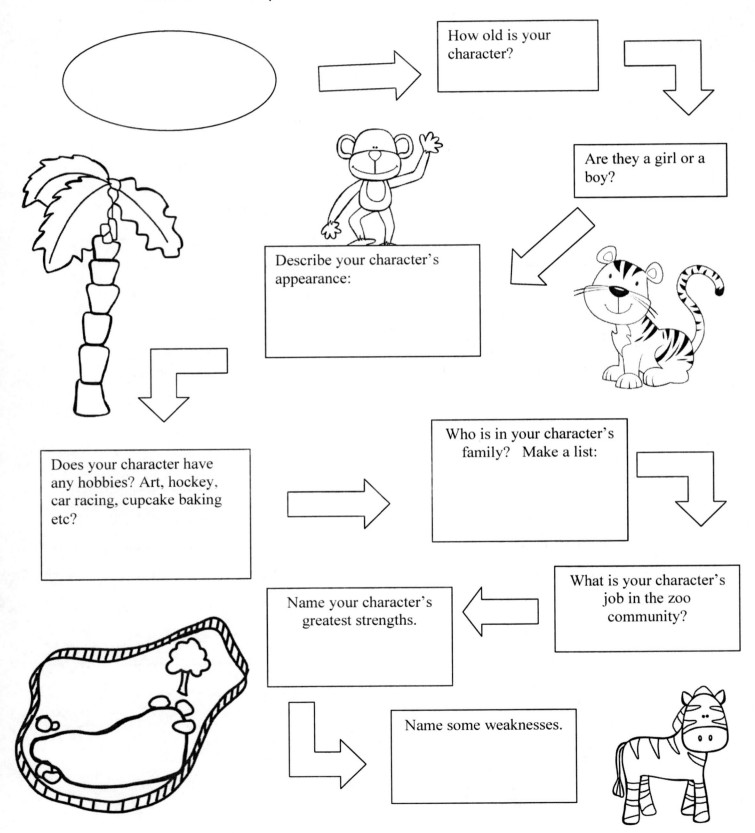

How old is your character?

Are they a girl or a boy?

Describe your character's appearance:

Does your character have any hobbies? Art, hockey, car racing, cupcake baking etc?

Who is in your character's family? Make a list:

What is your character's job in the zoo community?

Name your character's greatest strengths.

Name some weaknesses.

Lesson Two Teacher's Notes
Create a Setting

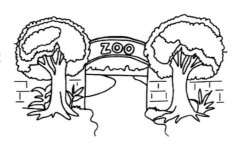

A setting is the time in history and the place where a story takes place. For this curriculum the setting is a zoo. It could be in a large city zoo with exotic animals, a small country zoo, or even a zoo on the planet Mars! It's important to describe the setting with vivid colors, sights, and sounds. **Encourage the students to use all five of their senses.** If there is more than one student, it's time to vote on the name of the zoo community where the characters live such as Animal Planet, Zany Zooville, etc.

Activity-Draw and Color a Map of the Zoo Community
Using the map on page 17, ask the students to draw a map of the zoo community. Draw pictures of their character and their habitat (along with other characters if you are using this with more than one student). Include the animal character's work places such as the bakery, city hall, sports complex etc.

Notes

_____

_____

_____

_____

_____

_____

_____

Lesson Two Handout
Create a Zoo Setting

A setting is the place and time in history where a story takes place. It could be in a city zoo, a country zoo, or even a zoo on Mars! It's important to describe the setting using vivid colors, sights, and sounds. Fill out the next several pages using all five or your senses.

Using your sense of sight, write in each balloon things you would see in a zoo. Include colors.

Using your sense of sound, write in each star a sound you might hear in a zoo.

Use your sense of taste to create fun "tasting" cereal for the animals:

Using your sense of smell, write in the clouds things you might smell at a zoo.

Use your sense of touch! What kinds of textures would you find at a zoo? Soft, hard, furry, smooth, bumpy, etc? Write them in the squares.

Draw a Map of the Zoo
Add Streets and Animals

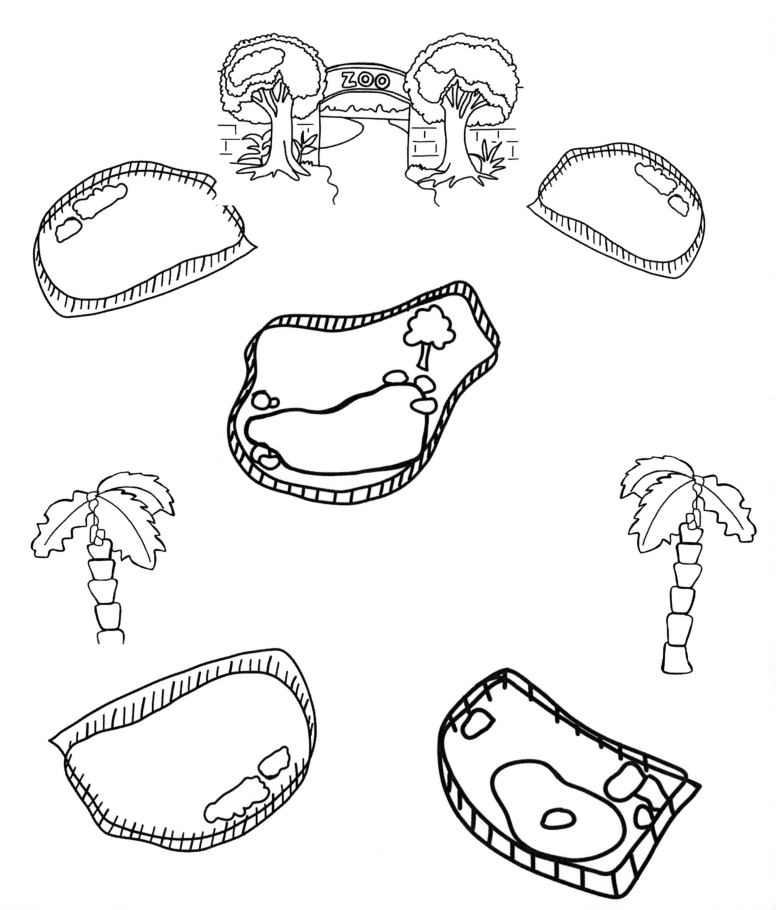

Lesson Three Teacher's Notes
Create a Plot

A plot is like writing your own recipe. Start with characters who want to reach a goal, add in a few obstacles to keep them from getting it, mix in some fun antics along the way, then help them reach their goal at the end. A good story will increase the tension by *almost* letting the characters solve their problem, but they fail in the first attempt. The story becomes even more exciting if they fail twice!

Have students fill out the 5 W's of a Plot.

Activity-Make Mix and Match Plot Cards

To generate story ideas cut out the cards on the next several pages. Color the animal cards and flip them over so you can't see them, then place them in a pile like a deck of cards. Cut out the plot cards. On the blank cards write down your own story problem ideas. Examples: someone gets lost, a bike is stolen, or they need money for something special, etc. Put all the plot cards together in another pile like a deck of cards. Flip them over so you can't read them. Draw one card from the animal pile. Then pick up two cards from the story problem pile.
Make up a story idea with the three cards.
Write down your idea in two to five sentences.

Notes

_____

_____

_____

_____

_____

_____

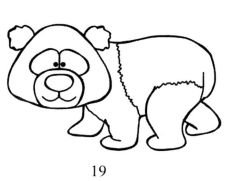

21

A large mysterious box arrives at the zoo. Write about what several characters think is inside. Perhaps some characters are excited and others are afraid. Maybe there can be a countdown of when it will be opened.

One of the animals invents a time machine. He can witness or affect a historical event to turn out differently: Be an animal on the Mayflower, the horse that Paul Revere rode, be the first animal to walk on the moon, etc.

One of the animals is secretly a super hero.

OR

All of the animals are secretly super heroes. Write about how they discover each other's super powers.

One of the characters invents a shrinking gun. Who and what does she shrink? Why? What else happens? Does another animal devise a plan to steal it? Does she use it for good or evil?

The zoo is closing down and all of the animals have to be shipped to other zoos all over the globe. In order to stop this and save the zoo, the animals devise a plan.

Someone sabotages the food supply. All the animals turn different colors and make other animal sounds instead of their own. Some get spots or stripes. Some can only sing or hiccup while bubbles pop out of their mouths!

Christmas is coming! All the animals are preparing for the holiday. Do they make advent wreaths and sing carols? Or send Christmas cards and one gets lost in the mail? Do they bake the world's largest gingerbread house?

One of the animals is a newspaper reporter. She uncovers several clues about a hidden treasure in the zoo. How do the animals respond to this news? Make up some fun clues.

A new animal comes to the zoo but he doesn't speak English! He seems to have important information for the zoo. How do the other animals reach out to him to communicate?

Lesson Three Handout #1
Create a Plot

Use the 5 W's to Create a Plot for your Zoo Adventure.

Who?

_____

_____

_____

Where? (Describe the setting)

_____

_____

_____

When?

_____

_____

_____

What's going to happen?

_____

_____

_____

_____

Why?

_____

_____

_____

_____

_____

Lesson Three Handout
#2 The "Build-Up"
Creates Suspense

In this part of the story, your character tries to solve the problem, but fails in the first several tries.

What is the problem?

_____

_____

How do they try to solve it?

_____

_____

Why does this fail?

_____

_____

How do they try to solve it again?

_____

_____

Do they succeed or have to try again?

_____

_____

If they have to try again, what happens?

_____

_____

_____

_____

Lesson Four Teacher's Notes
The Golden Rule-"Show, Don't Tell"

C.S. Lewis, author of the popular Chronicles of Narnia series, once said, "In writing, don't merely tell us how you want us to feel. . . I mean, instead of telling us a thing was "terrible," describe it so that we'll be terrified. Don't say it was "delightful"; make us say "delightful" when we've read the description." A good story describes the body language of the character's emotions, making the story come alive. This is the Golden Rule of Writing called "Show, Don't Tell."

Here are two examples of someone who is afraid:
1. Mickey the Monkey sat in the tree when all of a sudden he heard a booming noise. He was afraid. **These sentences TELL the reader he is afraid.**

2. Mickey the Monkey sat in the tree when all of a sudden he heard a booming noise. His heart pounded like a drum and the hairs on the top of his head stood up. **These sentences SHOW the reader his body language when he was afraid.**

Activity-Create a Zoo Setting Color Palette
Use a very large box of crayons. On a plain white piece of paper instruct the students to choose ten to fifteen colors they would find in a zoo. Then draw round circles of each color about the size of a walnut and label them. For fun: instead of circles they can make the icon a paw print. Have them use the exact names of the crayon color such as "chestnut" or "fuzzy-wuzzy brown" in their stories when describing animal colors instead of plain old brown. They can keep it in their zoo folder. This also builds their color vocabulary.

Notes
_____

_____

_____

Lesson Four Handout
Practice the Golden Rule
"Show, Don't Tell"

Write a sentence for each emotion showing the character's body language like the examples on the previous page.

Excitement

_____

_____

_____

_____

Curiosity

_____

_____

_____

_____

Anger

_____

_____

_____

_____

Fear

_____

_____

_____

_____

Pride

_____

_____

_____

_____

Happy

_____

_____

_____

_____

Sad

_____

_____

_____

_____

Lesson Five Teacher's Notes
Write the Beginning

Every story has three major parts: A beginning, middle, and an end.

The Beginning: The first sentences should start the story off right in the middle of interesting action to draw the reader in. This is called a HOOK. This should include your main character and the problem he or she faces.

The Middle of a story is where the character tries to solve the problem. It might even get worse. Think: drama, drama, drama! Some writers use the one, two, three method. The first two attempts to solve the problem fail and on the third try, the character succeeds.

The End is where the main characters overcome their problem. If it is a fable, they can grow in character in the process. If they start out fearful, they learn to be brave. If they start out selfish, they learn the joy of serving others.

*INSTRUCT THE STUDENTS TO SKIP A LINE when writing. It makes corrections and editing easier later.

Activity-Write a Hook and Share Ideas
Have each student write down one of the characters from the group on a piece of paper (it doesn't have to be their own character) and make up a story problem that they must solve. Collect all the ideas into a container and mix them up. Then have each student draw one out and write a hook according to what they drew out. Have the children read them aloud. If you are schooling one child, have them do the same by writing three to five story problems with characters and draw out one or two to write hooks to share with the teacher.

Lesson Five Handout
Write the Beginning of your Zoo Adventure

Can you begin your story with interesting action?
Write a HOOK for your story.

_____

_____

_____

_____

_____

_____

_____

_____

Every good story has a problem for the main character to solve. Write
several sentences showing the story problem either in your hook or
after it:

_____

_____

_____

_____

_____

_____

_____

_____

My Zany Zoo Adventure

_____

_____

_____

_____

_____

_____

_____

_____

_____

_____

_____

_____

_____

_____

_____

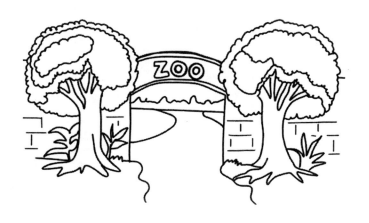

_____

_____

_____

_____

_____

_____

_____

_____

_____

_____

_____

_____

_____

_____

_____

_____

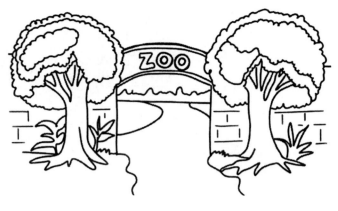

_____

_____

_____

_____

_____

_____

_____

_____

_____

_____

_____

_____

_____

_____

_____

_____

_____

_____

Lesson Six Teacher's Notes
Dialogue

Dialogue is when a person in a story is talking. Good dialogue adds interest and action to a story. Use quotation marks at the beginning, when the characters start to talk, and again at the end when they are finished talking. Put all ending punctuation marks (like periods, question marks, or exclamation marks) *inside* the quotation marks.

Example:
"Race you to the lion's den," said Micah Monkey.

There are two parts to a sentence of dialogue. The first part is the quote; the second part is the tag line. You separate them with a comma unless you use an exclamation or question mark.

Example:
"Race you to the lion's den," is the quotation.
'Said Micah Monkey' is the tag line. The first word in the tag line is never capitalized (unless it is proper noun like 'Micah Monkey said.')

There are many different ways to use "said" that can make your story come alive.

Example: Instead of using "said" in the above example you could say:

"Race you to the lion's den," **shouted** Micah Monkey.

This paints a vivid picture better than just saying "said." You can pepper fun tag lines throughout your story.

Activity-Mimic Tag Lines
Choose eight to ten tag lines from page 38 and write them down on a piece of paper. Cut them out and put them in a cup. Have the students draw them out one at a time and mimic how to say them. Everyone else guesses which one they are imitating.

Lesson Six Handout
Dialogue

Dialogue is when a person in your story is talking. Use quotation marks at the beginning, when your characters first start to talk, and again at the end when they are finished. Put all ending punctuation marks (like periods, question marks, or exclamation marks) *inside* the quotation marks.

Example:
    "Race you to the lion's den," said Micah Monkey.

Write this sentence: **Let's find some food said Kelly Kangaroo** on the line below using the correct dialogue punctuation:

_____

There are two parts to a sentence of dialogue. The first part is the quote; the second part is the tag line. You separate them with a comma unless you use an exclamation or questions mark.

Example:
    "Race you to the lion's den," is the quotation.
    "Said Micah Monkey" is the tag line.

What other tag line could you use for that same sentence?

_____

Example: Instead of using "said" in the above example you can say:

    "Race you to the lion's den," **shouted** Micah Monkey.

This paints a vivid picture better than just saying "said." You can pepper fun tag lines throughout your story.

Write a line of dialogue in each text box. Add quotation marks and a fun tag line. There is a list of tag lines on the following page.

Other Ways to Say "Said" in a Tag Line

admitted

agreed

answered

argued

asked

barked

begged

boasted

boomed

bragged

bellowed

blurted

complained

confessed

cried

defended

declared

demanded

denied

exclaimed

giggled

hesitated

hissed

hinted

hollered

howled

interrupted

joked

laughed

mumbled

muttered

nagged

objected

ordered

pleaded

promised

proclaimed

questioned

recalled

remembered

roared

scolded

scoffed

screamed

snarled

snorted

soothed

squawked

stammered

suggested

taunted

tattled

teased

whimpered

whooped

whispered

yapped

yakked

yelled

yelped

38

Lesson Seven Teacher's Notes
Write the Middle of Your Story

The middle of the story is where the characters try to reach their goal, but the writer puts an obstacle in their way. They should try several times but not succeed. Some writers say "think, drama, drama, drama!"

Activity-Brainstorm Ideas from the Create Tension Handout

Have the students read aloud what they have written on the handout, and then let others give them ideas on how to create tension in their stories. If you are schooling one student, have the child brainstorm with the teacher.

Activity-Story Balloon Bomb

Blow up six balloons. Write one of the questions from below on the bottom of each balloon using a permanent black marker. Toss the balloons around the room at the same time. Count down together: 5,4,3,2,1, and shout, "Balloon bomb!" Everyone drops to the floor and grabs the balloon nearest to them. Then the students must answer the question on the balloon. Questions:

- Describe the main character in your story.
- Describe the setting using all five of your senses.
- Show "happy" in a sentence (instead of telling).
- Show "anger" in a sentence (instead of telling).
- What is the main story problem?
- What is the solution?

Notes_____

_____

Lesson Seven Handout
Write the Middle of Your Story

What is your story problem?

_____

_____

List four ways the problem could get worse when the characters try to solve it. Maybe some of the ways can be funny.

1. _____
   _____
   _____

2. _____
   _____
   _____

3. _____
   _____
   _____

4. _____
   _____

Continue writing the middle of your story:

_____

_____

_____

_____

_____

_____

_____

_____

_____

_____

_____

_____

_____

_____

_____

_____

_____

Lesson Eight Teacher's Notes
Stage Directions

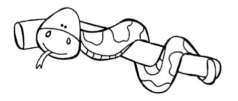

In every play the script tells the characters where to stand or what actions to perform while they are talking. This is called stage directions. In writing we can add stage directions to dialogue to give a better picture of what is going on in the story.

Example:
    "Race you to the lion's den!" shouted Micah Monkey, **swinging on the tree branch.**
    "Swinging on a tree branch" is the stage direction. It tells the reader what Micah Monkey is doing while he is talking.

Today the student will practice writing stage directions. Encourage them to use them as they continue writing their stories for fifteen to twenty minutes.

Activity-Charades
Cut out the stage directions on page 47. Place them in a cup and have each student draw one out. They must act out the stage direction, and everyone else should guess what they are doing.

Notes

_____

_____

_____

_____

_____

Lesson Eight Handout
Stage Directions

In every play the script tells the characters where to stand or what actions to perform while they are talking. This is called "stage directions." In writing we can add stage directions to dialogue to give a better picture of what is going on in the story.

Example 1:

"Race you to the lion's den!" shouted Micah Monkey, **swinging on the tree branch.**

"Swinging on a tree branch" is the stage direction. It tells the reader what Micah Monkey is doing while he is talking.

Example 2:

"Oh no! I'm late!" shouted Janet Giraffe **as she grabbed her back pack and dashed off to meet her friend.**

The words "as she grabbed her back pack and dashed off to catch the school bus" is the stage direction. It tells the reader what she was doing as she was speaking.

Practice Writing Dialogue with Stage Directions:

Have your characters greet each other using dialogue and stage directions. Then draw a picture underneath the sentences showing what they are doing. Continue onto the next page.

_____

_____

_____

_____

Have two characters talk while they are playing a sport together using dialogue and stage directions. Then draw a picture underneath the sentences showing what they are doing.

_____

_____

_____

_____

Have your characters chat while they eat breakfast using dialogue and stage directions. Then draw a picture underneath the sentences showing what they are doing.

_____

_____

_____

_____

Cut out Stage Directions for Charades

Swinging on a tree branch

Splashing in the pool

Hopping to eat lunch

Licking his fur

Waddling down the path

Roaring as he walked

Picking the fur on the monkey in front of her and eating it

Clapping and Jumping up and down

Lesson Nine Teacher's Notes
Write the End of the Story

Ending a story is when you help the characters reach their goal. If you want them to learn a good life lesson then it's also time to give them an "ah-ha" moment, when the characters realize they have learned something.

Activity- Illustrate Zoo Characters Using Marble Painting

Use a large shirt box (8.5 x 11 or larger), washable paints, and marbles. Have the student trace around the outside edge of the whole animal of his choice from the Animal Information Station pages (beginning on page 61). Then cut it out. Save the outer piece of paper – there should be cut-out silhouette of the animal in the middle of the white paper. Tape down a colored sheet of construction paper that closely matches the natural color of the animal on the inside of the box. Over that paper, tape down your silhouette cut-out animal. Squirt a nickel size of paint in various colors on top of the animal cut-out. Drop your marbles in the box and roll them around in the box over the paints until all of the white space of the cut-out is filled in. Let dry. Pull the white silhouette cut-out off then pull the newly painted picture on the construction paper off the box. It should have the shape of the animal with a marble painting on it. Hang it up or save it in your folder to add to your story later.

Notes

_____

_____

_____

_____

_____

_____

_____

Lesson Nine Handout
Write the End to Your Story:
Your Character Reaches His Goal

_____

_____

_____

_____

_____

_____

_____

_____

_____

_____

_____

_____

_____

_____

_____

_____

_____

_____

_____

_____

_____

_____

_____

_____

_____

_____

_____

_____

_____

_____

_____

_____

_____

_____

_____

Lesson Ten Teacher's Notes
Spice Up Your Story

Now that the students are finished writing their story, it's time to spice it up a bit. Adding adjectives to the nouns in a story helps to create a vivid picture in the reader's mind. This also helps the reader to experience the story, not just read it.

A noun is a person, place, or thing.
An adjective is a word used to describe a noun. It can tell which one, what kind, how many, what color, what texture, etc.

Activity - Have the Students Illustrate
a scene from their story with colored pencils. They can add it to their zoo folder.

Notes

_____

_____

_____

_____

_____

_____

_____

_____

Lesson Ten Handout
Spice Up Your Story

Add an adjective in each of the blanks below for practice:

1. Mickey the Monkey smelled the _____ flowers in the _____ tree.

2. The _____ kangaroo hopped across the _____ yard to greet her _____ friend.

3. The _____ shark brigade protected the _____ sunken ship.

4. Tina the Tiger baked her favorite _____ cupcakes for the party.

5. Pearl the Porpoise blows _____ bubbles when she is happy.

6. The two _____ zebras ran as fast as they could when they saw the _____ lion.

7. The _____ penguins played in the _____ water.

8. Bart the Bear clicked his _____ claws.

9. The frightened gazelle hid when he heard a _____ noise.

10. The _____ giraffes reached for the _____ food.

Lesson Eleven Teacher's Notes
Edit Your Story

Many great writers revise their stories ten to twenty times! We will only revise this story once. Here is a list to help your students check off their edits as they complete them. After the students have checked them off, they can neatly rewrite their story with all the corrections in it. They can use the fun, decorated paper beginning on page 81.

Activity- Illustrate another Scene
Have the students illustrate another scene from their story with colored pencils and add it to their zoo folder.

Notes

_____

_____

_____

_____

_____

_____

_____

_____

_____

_____

_____

Lesson Eleven Handout
Final Editing and Revising

_____1. Add at least one adjective to every other sentence in your story. An adjective is a word that describes a person, place or thing: color, size, texture, etc.

_____2. Check every sentence making sure it begins with a capital letter and ends with a period, question mark, or exclamation point.

_____3. Can you combine any two shorter sentences and make them into one longer one? For example: Dana runs fast. Dana plays soccer. To combine: Dana runs fast when she plays soccer.

_____4. Are all the punctuation marks in your dialogue inside the quotation marks? Make sure there is a comma between the line of dialogue and the dialogue tag.

_____5. Check your spelling

_____6. Did you "Show and not Tell" in places?

_____7. Have you used all five senses when describing the setting somewhere in your story?

- o Sights _____
- o Sounds_____
- o Tastes _____
- o Smells _____
- o Touch _____

Lesson Twelve Teacher's Notes
Put it all Together

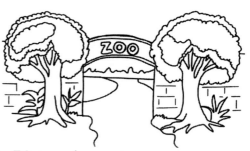

Let each student fill in the cover template on page 59 to color and create a title page with a catchy title.

Tear out the final written story from the book and trim off any ragged edges. Number the pages. Using a three-hole punch, help students assemble their stories and any illustrations they have into a plastic essay binder. These can be found at a superstore or office supply store.

Activity-Flashlight Theatre

Choose a table or comfy family room chair. Turn out the lights and flash several flashlights on the reader as each student takes turns reading their stories. For a fun option, cut out a large square from a large box making it look like a TV. Add paint or glitter. Make popcorn or another fun snack. Have the reader sit behind it and read. As an option let them dress up in fun costumes, hats, or glasses. This is always a highlight! Share **good flashlight behavior** beforehand: No flashing in anyone's eyes or waving them around to make fun patterns on the wall. Invite grandparents, friends, or neighbors.

Notes

_____

_____

_____

_____

_____

_____

_____

Flashlight Theater

Chocolaty Peanut Butter Popcorn Recipe:

- Dump 8 cups popped popcorn in a bowl
- Cook 1/2 cup honey and 1/3 cup granulated sugar until it boils – simmer 2 minutes
- Take off heat and mix in 1/2 cup peanut butter until melted
- Add 1/2 teaspoon vanilla extract and pour mixture over popcorn and stir – spread onto cookie sheet
- Melt 1/2 cup milk chocolate chips and drizzle over – let sit until chocolate hardens – scoop into large bowl
- Add 1 1/2 cups Mini Reese's Peanut Butter Cups and toss
- Enjoy! ☺

Yummy Pizza Popcorn Recipe:

- Use microwave popcorn or pop your own!
- Drizzle melted butter over the top and toss
- Sprinkle on garlic powder, oregano and parmesan cheese
- Optional – add cut up cooked pepperoni slices or bacon
- Toss together

_____

By

_____

Zoo Animal Information-Station Sheets

Toucan
Scientific Family-Bird

Native of South America's tropical forests typically, but they can be found everywhere.

Fun Fact- Toucans nest in tree holes. Usually they will have two to four eggs each year. Both parents care for the eggs. Young toucans do not have a large bill at birth—it grows as they develop and will not become full sized for several months.

Gorilla
Scientific Family-Mammal

Native of Africa in the mountains or lowlands.

Fun Fact- Gorillas can climb trees but are usually found on the ground in families of up to thirty. Each family of gorillas is led by the strongest older male gorilla called a "silver back," whose back has silver on it.

Kangaroo
Scientific Family-Mammal

Native of forests, desserts, and open grasslands of Australia and forests of Tasmania.

Fun Fact- Kangaroos' legs cannot move separately from one another, so they have to hop everywhere. They're pretty fast and can reach speeds of over 35 miles (56 kilometers) an hour and jump 25 feet (8 meters) in a single leap.

Elephant
Scientific Family-Mammal

Native of Africa and Asia

Fun Fact- African elephants are the largest land animals on Earth. They are a little bit bigger than their cousins in Asia. You can tell the difference between African and Asian elephants by looking at their ears. African elephants can have ears that are larger and look somewhat like the continent of Africa. Asian elephants have smaller ears that are round.

Crocodile
Scientific Family-Reptile

Native of North and South America, Africa, South East Asia, and Australia.

Fun Fact- The largest crocodiles on Earth are saltwater crocs, or "salties," as they're called in Australia. They are amazing swimmers and can even be spotted far out at sea.

Lion

Scientific Family-Mammal

Native of Africa and Asia.

Fun Fact- Female lions are the main hunters. They often work together to catch antelopes, zebras, wildebeest, and other large animals of the open grasslands. Many of these animals are actually faster than lions, which is why the lions must work together to catch dinner.

Hippopotamus
Scientific Family-Mammal

Native of Africa.

Fun Fact- Hippopotamuses love water. The Greeks named them the "river horse." Hippos spend up to sixteen hours a day underwater. They swim in rivers and lakes to keep their big bodies cool under the hot African sun.

Sea Turtle
Scientific Family-Reptile

Native of all over the world.

Fun Fact- Most sea turtles will warm themselves by swimming close to the surface of shallow waters. One turtle, the Eastern Pacific green sea turtle, will go to land to bask in the sun. Sometimes the green sea turtle can be seen sunbathing alongside seals and albatrosses. Most other turtles only go on land to nest.

Giraffe
Scientific Family-Mammal

Native of African grasslands.

Fun Fact- Giraffes are the world's tallest mammals. Their long legs and necks are what make them so tall. A giraffe's legs alone are taller than most humans at about six feet. These long legs enable giraffes to run as fast as 35 miles per hour for short runs and cruise easily at 10 miles per hour for longer runs.

Flamingo
Scientific Family-Bird

Native of all over the world in warmer regions.

Fun Fact- The bent bill of a Flamingo allows them to feed on tiny organisms like plankton, tiny fish, and fly larvae. Shrimplike crustaceans are the cause for the flamingo's pink color. When flamingos are kept in captivity they are pale, unless their diets are altered.

71

Zebra
Scientific Family-Mammal

Native of Africa.

Fun Fact- Like the fingerprints of humans, each zebra has his or her own stripe pattern. No two zebras' stripes are alike.

Monkey
Scientific Family-Mammal

Native of Africa, Asia, and Central and South America.

Fun Fact- There are over 264 species of monkeys in the world. Groups of monkeys are known as a tribe, a troop, or a mission. Different monkey species eat all kinds of different foods. Some eat fruit, insects, flowers, leaves, or reptiles.

Giant Panda
Scientific Family-Mammal

Native of Asia (where there is lots of bamboo!)

Fun Fact- Pandas *love* to eat bamboo. They eat it for twelve hours each day. It takes about twenty-eight pounds of bamboo for a Panda to be full. There are only about 1,000 Giant Pandas left in the wild and about 100 in zoos.

Peacock
Scientific Family-Bird

Native of India, Pakistan, Sri Lanka, Southeast Asia, and central Africa.

Fun Fact- Though most people say "peacocks," that's only the correct name for the male of this type of bird. Females are called "peahens," and the whole group is called "peafowl."

Penguin
Scientific Family-Bird

Native of the southern hemisphere (none live at the North Pole).

Fun Fact- Penguins live up to 80 percent of their lives in the ocean. It is a myth that they can live in cold temperatures. Some penguins, like the Galapagos penguins, live on tropical islands near the equator.

Grizzly Bear
Scientific Family-Mammal

Native of North America.

Fun Fact- Even though grizzly bears are powerful and fast predators, much of their diets consist of berries, nuts, leaves, fruit, and roots. They can run at 30 miles per hour if they need to, even though they weigh around 800 pounds!

Seals
Scientific Family-Mammal

Native of the cold Arctic Ocean waters, coasts of Antarctica, Northern Pacific Ocean, the coasts of South America, Africa, and southern Australia.

Fun Fact- Seals are mammals in a group called "pinnipeds," which means "fin-footed." There are eighteen species of true seals and sixteen species of eared seals. Seven of the eared species are sea lions.

Boa Constricter
Scientific Family-Reptile

Native of South America, Central America, and Mexico.

Fun Fact- Boas are not poisonous and can grow to up to thirteen feet long. Boas are able to swallow their prey whole because their jaws can stretch. They will eat anything, like wild pigs, monkeys, rodents, and birds. The biggest Boa ever found was eighteen feet long!

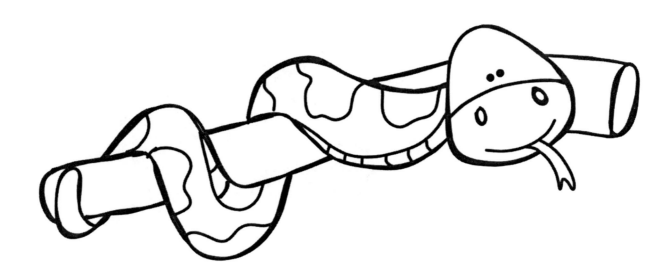

Tiger
Scientific Family-Mammal

Native of Asia, Siberian tigers live in Russia and China

Fun Fact- Tigers are the largest felines in the world. There are more tigers in captivity than there are in the wild. Only 3,200 tigers live in the wild, while 5,000 live in captivity. Just like zebras, a tiger's stripes are unique, and no two tigers have the same pattern.

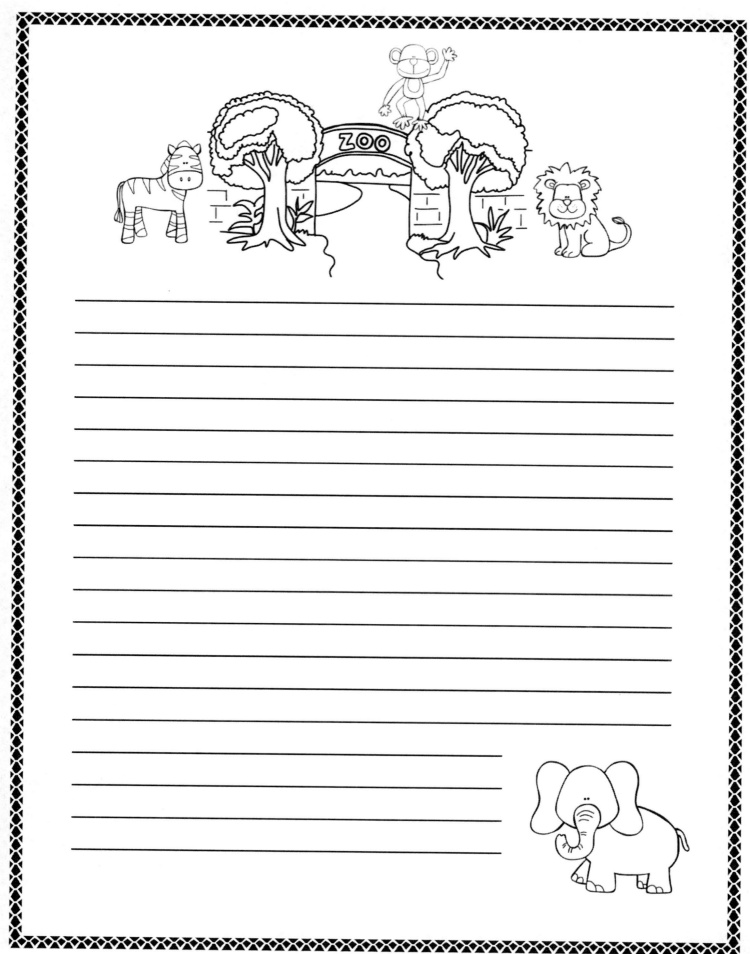

About the Author

Jan May loved homeschooling her two children. Whether it was attending re-enactments of the Revolutionary War or collecting an amphibian zoo, hands-on education was always at the forefront of her curriculum. She is author of the *Creative Writing Made Easy* series that engages even the most reluctant writers! All of the books are filled with fun interactive language activities involving each type of learner: visual, auditory and kinesthetic. Having been a creative writing teacher for over fifteen years, she believes that given the right tools, every child can learn to write and love it!

Visit her website for fun crafts and recipes for kids and for her online schedule inspiring high school teens to deepen their fiction writing. www.NewMillenniumGirlBooks.com

Look for other books in this themed writing series and turn writing time into a delight!

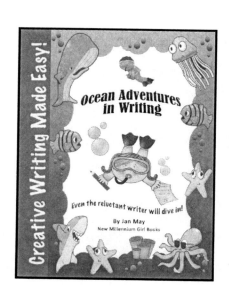